# WALT DISNEY PICTURES'

# THE BLACK CAULDRON

SCHOLASTIC INC

New York Toronto London Auckland Sydney

ISBN: 0-590-33796-3

12 11 10 9 8 7 6 5 4 3 2 1    7    5 6 7 8 9/8 0/9
Printed in the U.S.A.

ONCE UPON A TIME, IN OLD PRYDAIN, THERE LIVED AN OLD AND WISE SORCERER NAMED DALLBEN, AND HIS APPRENTICE, TARAN.

LIFE WAS GOOD IN PRYDAIN UNTIL THE HORNED KING, A VICIOUS LORD, AROSE TO THREATEN THE PEACE. THE EVIL MONARCH'S ACTIVITIES WORRIED DALLBEN...

TARAN, ON THE OTHER HAND, WAS UNCONCERNED. ALL HE COULD THINK ABOUT WAS THE GLORY OF BATTLE...

TARAN! STOP YOUR DAYDREAMING AND GIVE SOME THOUGHT TO HEN WEN! IT'S TIME FOR HER BREAKFAST!

IT'S ALWAYS HEN WEN! WHAT'S SO SPECIAL ABOUT A PIG?

SOMEDAY YOU WILL FIND OUT HOW IMPORTANT SHE IS!

I'M NOT A CHILD, I'M A WARRIOR! PRYDAIN NEEDS HEROES, AND I SHALL BE ONE!

I WON'T SPEND MY LIFE TAKING CARE OF A PIG!

I'M A FIGHTER, NOT A PIG KEEPER!

WHOEVER SAYS OTHERWISE—TAKE THAT!

AT LAST WE MEET, HORNED KING! EN GARDE! THIS WILL BE A DUEL TO THE DEATH!

DID YOU SEE, HEN WEN? THEY'RE ALL AFRAID OF ME, EVEN THE HORNED KING!

OW!

PRYDAIN'S GREATEST WARRIOR... DRAWS HIS LAST BREATH!

HMM... OUR HERO TAKES A MUD-BATH, EH?

OH! DALLBEN! UM... I'M NO HERO— JUST A PIG KEEPER!

IT IS AN HONOR TO TAKE CARE OF HEN WEN! SHE IS NO ORDINARY PIG! NOW, GIVE HER A BATH!

I WISH I KNEW WHAT WAS SO SPECIAL ABOUT YOU, HEN!

I GUESS YOU AREN'T GOING TO TELL ME, ARE YOU? NOW WHAT'S WRONG?

HIIIIIII!

HEN WEN!

HIIIIII!!

DALLBEN! HEN WEN'S GONE CRAZY!

QUICK, LAD, BRING HER INSIDE! I FEARED THIS WOULD HAPPEN!

WHAT YOU ARE ABOUT TO SEE, TARAN, YOU MUST NEVER REVEAL TO ANYONE! NOW, PUT HER DOWN!

AN IMAGE IS TAKING SHAPE!

IT'S THE **HORNED KING!** HE'S SEARCHING!

THE **BLACK CAULDRON!** SO THAT'S IT!

AN AWESOME WEAPON, TARAN! IF THE HORNED KING UNLEASHES ITS POWER, NOTHING CAN STAND AGAINST IT! AND HEN WEN KNOWS WHERE IT IS!

THE HORNED KING HAS DISCOVERED HER POWERS! HE KNOWS THAT SHE CAN TELL HIM HOW TO FIND THE CAULDRON!

YOU MUST TAKE HER DEEP INTO THE FORBIDDEN FOREST! KEEP HER SAFE UNTIL I COME FOR YOU! COURAGE, LAD!

I'M NOT AFRAID, DALLBEN!

SO MUCH RESPONSIBILITY TO REST ON YOUNG SHOULDERS!

GOSH, HEN, I NEVER KNEW YOU COULD CREATE VISIONS! DALLBEN WON'T BE SORRY HE PLACED HIS TRUST IN ME, YOU WAIT AND SEE!

HE DID THE RIGHT THING! DON'T WORRY, HEN, YOU'RE UNDER THE PROTECTION OF PRYDAIN'S GREATEST WORRIOR!

TARAN OF CAER DALLBEN! TARAN THE HERO! THE GREATEST WARRIOR IN ALL PRYDAIN!

AND I COULDN'T HAVE DONE IT WITHOUT THE HELP OF MY PIG... HEN WEN?

HEN WEN?! OH, NO! SHE'S GONE! WHERE CAN SHE BE HIDING? HEN WEN! COME BACK HERE!

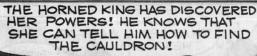

HEN WEN! LOOK— I'VE BROUGHT YOU A NICE, JUICY APPLE!

YES, YES! JUICY APPLE! GURGI LOVE!

HEY! GIVE BACK THAT APPLE!

APPLE? WHAT APPLE? GURGI NOT HAVE APPLE!

GIVE IT BACK! OR YOU'LL BE SORRY!

SHAME ON YOU! THAT APPLE WAS FOR HEN WEN!

GURGI SORRY! MASTER FORGIVE HIM?

OH, STOP IT! TELL ME — HAVE YOU SEEN MY PIG?

PIGGY... WITH CURLY TAIL? BIG EARS? YES, GURGI SEE, MASTER! COME!

HEN WEN!

KRiiiH KRiii

Hiii!

Hiiiiiiii

From the top of the crag, Taran spies a sinister fortress—the Horned King's lair...

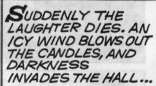

I **THOUGHT** I HEARD A NOISE...

OH! ARE YOU A PRISONER HERE, TOO?

I... UM... YES!

WHAT AN AWFUL PLACE!

I AM A PRINCESS, YOU KNOW! ARE YOU A PRINCE OR A KNIGHT?

NEITHER! I'M JUST AN ASSISTANT PIG KEEPER!

OH! I WAS HOPING YOU COULD HELP ME ESCAPE! YOU MAY COME WITH ME, IF YOU LIKE!

COME WITH YOU? BUT...

OF COURSE! DO YOU KNOW WHY THAT HATEFUL KING LOCKED ME UP?

HE THOUGHT MY BAUBLE COULD HELP HIM FIND A SILLY OLD CAULDRON! HE WAS WRONG!

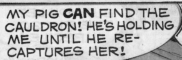

MY PIG **CAN** FIND THE CAULDRON! HE'S HOLDING ME UNTIL HE RE-CAPTURES HER!

WELL, COME ALONG! WE MUSTN'T TARRY!

THIS MUST BE A BURIAL CHAMBER!

RUMBLE!

LOOK!

HE MUST HAVE BEEN A GREAT WARRIOR!

YES! PERHAPS EVEN THE KING WHO BUILT THIS CASTLE!

LISTEN! SOMEONE'S COMING!

COME ON! PUT YOUR BACK INTO IT!

GOOD—THEY DIDN'T NOTICE US! BUT WE MUST GET AWAY QUICKLY!

WAIT! ARE YOU CRAZY? WHY HAVE YOU TAKEN THAT SWORD?

WE MIGHT NEED A WEAPON!

OH! MY BAUBLE!

IT'S GETTING AWAY! WE'LL BE CAUGHT!

NOOO! I'M **NOT** A SPY! I'M A BARD!

BE CAREFUL! YOU'RE MISTREATING THE HANDS OF AN ARTIST!

I'M NOT THE ONE YOU'RE LOOKING FOR!

HOW DARE YOU! I AM FFLEWDDUR FFLAM, MINSTREL OF MINSTRELS! I HAVE SUNG IN THE GRANDEST COURTS!

WELL, I WAS ONLY WAITING FOR AN INVITATION!

AS IF THINGS WEREN'T BAD ENOUGH...

HELLO! I AM PRINCESS EILONWY!

AND I'M TARAN, OF CAER DALLBEN!

MEANWHILE, OUR HEROES TAKE REFUGE IN THE FOREST...

BRAVO, FFLEWDDUR! THAT'S... UM... TUNEFUL!

THANK YOU, MY DEAR! YOU MAKE ME HOPE THAT THE NAME OF FFLAM WILL BE REMEMBERED!

ALMOST FINISHED, FFLEWDDUR! WHAT DO YOU THINK?

MARVELOUS, PRINCESS! WHAT PROOF OF YOUR KINDNESS! I SHALL COMPOSE A SONG...

OOPS!

I BEG YOUR PARDON, PRINCESS!

YOU REALLY SHOULD SING ABOUT OUR HEROIC ESCAPE!

GOOD IDEA! "IN THE DUNGEON, FEAR HELD US FAST..."

NOT ME! I WASN'T AFRAID!

OH, NO? YOU RAN PRETTY FAST FROM THE GUARDS!

I STOOD UP TO THEM, TOO! AFTER I GOT HEN WEN SAFE, I WENT BACK AND I...

...AND YOU BROUGHT THE GUARDS TO THEIR KNEES!

IT WAS THE MAGIC SWORD, AS MUCH AS YOU!

WHAT DOES A GIRL KNOW?

WITHOUT THIS "GIRL," YOU'D STILL BE IN THE DUNGEON!

SOME WARRIOR YOU ARE!

PRINCESS EILONWY! TARAN! PLEASE — DON'T QUARREL!

BUT THE HORNED KING KNOWS WHAT TARAN IS PLANNING...

YOU MUST FIND THE CAULDRON BEFORE HE DOES!

YES, MAJESTY, I WON'T FAIL YOU THIS TIME!

IN A HUGH UNDERGROUND CHAMBER, THE BODIES OF LONG-DEAD WARRIORS WAIT...

AAH... MY SOLDIERS! SOON THE BLACK CAULDRON WILL RETURN YOU TO LIFE!

THEN I SHALL RULE THE WORLD! SOON...YESSS! SSSOON!

MEANWHILE, TARAN AND HIS FRIENDS HAVE REACHED THE MARSHES OF MORVA...

SO FAR WE'VE FOUND NOTH-ING!

I WISH THIS FELLOW WOULD QUIT MAKING FUN OF US!

GO ON— YOU'LL SEE!

IF YOU SAY S...

FFLEWDDUR!

HA, HA, HA, HA, HA!

FFLEWDDUR!

No!

YOU'RE NOT GOING TO EAT THIS ONE!

HE'S MY SWEETIE-PIE!

ORWEN, YOU FORGET YOURSELF! YOU'RE A WITCH!

OH, ORGOCH—YOU CAN BE SO HATEFUL!

COME NOW—YOU'RE A BARD AGAIN!

HA, HA, HA! HEE, HEE! WE HAVEN'T HAD THIS MUCH FUN IN YEARS!

HA, HA!

STOP IT! WE'VE COME TO GET THE BLACK CAULDRON!

THE CAULDRON! NO ONE HAS ASKED FOR IT FOR OVER 2,000 YEARS!

IT MUST BE A TRICK!

I'LL HANDLE THIS!

PERHAPS YOU WILL FIND SOMETHING YOU WANT IN HERE!

DID YOU FIND WHAT YOU WANTED?

TARAN'S MAGIC SWORD LEAPS OUT OF HIS HAND AND...

I'VE NEVER SEEN THE LIKE!

WHEW!

WE MUST HAVE THAT SWORD!

LET'S MAKE HIM A LITTLE DEAL!

HEE, HEE!

SO, YOU WANT THE CAULDRON, DO YOU?

YES!

YOU'LL GIVE IT TO US?!

I DIDN'T SAY GIVE...BUT WE'LL TRADE...

MY SWORD? NEVER!

THE LANDSCAPE NOW IS DESOLATE—NOTHING LIVES...

WOW!

RUMBLE! RUMBLE!

LOOK!

RUMBLE! RUMBLE! RUMBLE!

THE BLACK CAULDRON!

WE MUST DESTROY IT!

CRACK!

BONG!

UNNH!

WE CAN'T DO IT! IT'S INDESTRUCTIBLE!

OOH!

HA, HA, HA, HA! YOU GOT WHAT YOU WANTED, DUCKIES!

THE CAULDRON CAN NEVER BE DESTROYED! BUT ITS POWER CAN BE STOPPED!

HOW?

A LIVING BEING MUST JUMP INTO IT OF HIS OWN FREE WILL!

YOU NEVER TOLD US THAT BEFORE!

A DEAL IS A DEAL! IT'S NOT OUR FAULT IF YOU DON'T KNOW WHAT YOU BARGAINED FOR! HA, HA, HA!

FOOLISH HUMANS! I'VE DONE MY PART! YOU'D BETTER COLLECT YOUR PIG! I'M GOING BACK!

DOLI IS RIGHT! IT'S ALL MY FAULT! I'M ONLY AN ASSISTANT PIG KEEPER!

NO, TARAN! YOU'RE NOT JUST A PIG KEEPER! BELIEVE IN YOURSELF — I DO!

HONEST, EILONWY?

HONEST, TARAN!

YOU... I... WE...UH...

SMACK!

HEE, HEE! HEE!

THE TWO OF YOU ARE TRUE FRIENDS! BUT YOU HAVE DONE ENOUGH! NOW...

SCREEE!

LOOK!

LET'S GET OUT OF HERE!

A THICK LIQUID BUBBLES FROM THE CAULDRON AND FLOWS DOWN OVER THE BODIES OF THE DEAD WARRIORS...

HOW HORRIBLE! I CAN'T WATCH!

RISING FROM THE INFERNAL BREW, A MIGHTY ARMY MARCHES FORTH...

WHAT A SAD END FOR US! AT LEAST WE'RE TOGETHER!

AH, MY WARRIORS! AN UNBELIEVABLE ARMY! GO OUT—AND DESTROY EVERYTHING IN YOUR PATH!

WHAT A SIGHT! COME, SIRE—WATCH FROM UP HERE!

THE AWFUL ARMY MARCHES OUT OF THE HORNED KING'S CITADEL ON ITS MISSION OF DEATH...

THE HOUR OF MY TRIUMPH IS HERE!

HOW SWEET IT IS!

BUT BRAVE LITTLE GURGI HAS NOT FORGOTTEN HIS FRIENDS...

GURGI! WHAT ARE YOU DOING HERE?

MASTER!

HOW DID YOU FIND US?

GURGI NOT ABANDON FRIENDS!

THANK YOU!

EILONWY, YOU AND FFLEWDDUR LEAVE WITH GURGI! I MUST STOP THE CAULDRON!

TARAN! NO! DON'T DO IT!

I AM SORRY, PRINCESS — IT IS THE PRICE I MUST PAY!

NO, TARAN! WAIT!

NO, MASTER! GURGI NOT LET YOU JUMP INTO WICKED CAULDRON!

GURGI! LET ME PASS!

NO! YOUR FRIENDS NEED YOU! I AM THE ONE TO DO THIS!

GURGI! NO!

*THANKS TO GURGI, THE AWFUL BREW BEGINS TO COOL, AN ICY VAPOR WAFTS FROM THE CAULDRON...*

*THE CAULDRON NO LONGER GIVES LIFE TO THE HORNED KING'S SOLDIERS...*

SIRE! SOME-THING'S WRONG!

NO! IT CAN'T BE!

IT'S YOUR FAULT!

NO, SIRE! NO! UNGGH!

GO WITH FFLEWDDUR, EILONWY! THERE MAY STILL BE A CHANCE TO SAVE GURGI!

PLEASE, TARAN! DON'T GO!

*THE ICY BLAST DRAWS TARAN IRRESISTIBLY TOWARD THE BLACK CAULDRON...*

NO, SIRE! NOT IN THE CAULDRON!

GET UP!

DO WHAT HE SAYS!

LOOK, SIRE—THE PIG BOY! THIS IS HIS FAULT!

YOU WON'T ESCAPE ME THIS TIME!

A MUFFLED ROAR SHAKES THE CASTLE, AND THE WALLS BEGIN TO CRUMBLE...

EILONWY! FFLEWDDUR!

TARAN!

THANK HEAVEN YOU'RE SAFE! QUICK! WE MUST GET AWAY!

COURAGE, FFLEWDDUR! YOU MUST JUMP ACROSS!

LOOK! A BOAT!

PUSH, FFLEWDDUR!

OH, NO! THE GATE IS CLOSED!

HURRY, TARAN! EVERYTHING'S FALLING APART!

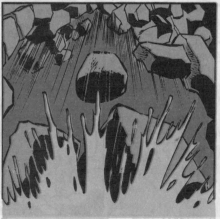

SWEPT AWAY FROM THE CASTLE ON A HUGH WAVE, TARAN AND HIS FRIENDS WATCH THE CASTLE BURN TO ASHES...

ONLY CREEPER ESCAPES...

LOOK! THE CAULDRON!

POOR GURGI! IT'S ALL MY FAULT!

DON'T BLAME YOURSELF!

WELL, WELL— WHY ARE OUR HEROES SO SAD?

GURGI IS THE HERO!

LEAVE US ALONE, YOU HAGS!

HE'S SO CUTE WHEN HE'S ANGRY!

YOU WANTED THE BLACK CAULDRON, AND WE GAVE IT TO YOU! NOW WE'LL TAKE IT BACK!

OH, NO! WE WON'T GIVE SOMETHING FOR NOTHING! BUT WE WILL TRADE...

TRADE?!

I GET IT! HA, HA, HA!

HE'S A CLEVER FELLOW, HE IS! HA, HA, HA!

YOU LITTLE IMP! YOU WERE FAKING!

HE'S ALIVE! GURGI'S ALIVE!

OH, THANK HEAVEN!

I'M ALIVE!

GURGI SO HAPPY TO BE BACK WITH HIS FRIENDS!

I SHALL COMPOSE A BALLAD ABOUT OUR WONDERFUL ADVENTURE...

MY HARP! THAT'S THE FIRST TIME IT'S GIVEN ME ANY ENCOURAGEMENT!

COME WITH ME! WE WILL ALL GO BACK TO CAER DALLBEN!

BUT DALLBEN ALREADY KNOWS THAT PEACE HAS COME TO THE KINGDOM OF PRYDAIN!